D0284700

A PARRAGON BOOK

Published by Parragon Book Service Ltd,
Units 13-17, Avonbridge Trading Estate, Atlantic Road,
Avonmouth, Bristol BS11 9QD

Produced by The Templar Company plc,
Pippbrook Mill, London Road, Dorking,
Surrey RH4 1JE

Written by Godfrey Hall and Robert Snedden
Series Editor Robert Snedden
Designed by Mark Summersby
Illustrated by Julian Baker

Printed and bound in the UK

ISBN 0 7525 1673 6

FACTFINDERS

·NATURAL·
DISASTERS

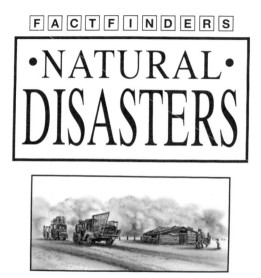

·PARRAGON·

CONTENTS

INTRODUCTION

The enormous energy unleashed by earthquakes, volcanic eruptions, hurricanes and other natural disasters can leave people feeling helpless against the powerful forces of nature. Throughout most of human history, these devastating experiences have been considered 'acts of God', with no hope of predicting them or preparing for them. Although we now have an understanding of how an earthquake happens or why a volcano erupts these are still awesome events, for all our ability to set down some sort of explanation for them.

In the past hundred years a million people have died in earthquakes, another million have been killed by hurricanes and tornadoes and 9 million have lost their lives in floods. In addition to this many millions more have died as a result of famine and disease, often brought about by another natural catastrophe. We should also not forget the long-term disasters, particularly drought. In many of the world's countries chronic water shortage is a fact of life, especially in the African Sahel region bordering the Sahara desert. The numbers of people whose lives are affected by natural disasters runs into the hundreds of millions.

Today, the 100 most dangerous volcanoes in the world have been identified and are continually monitored by satellites and ground instruments, providing a crucial early warning for millions of people around the world.

When Mount Pinatubo erupted in the Philippines in June 1991 only about 800 people died because American and Filipino teams of volcano watchers had correctly predicted the eruption and ensured that thousands of residents were evacuated from the area in time.

Under a UN initiative, poorer countries have been helped with earthquake engineering and hurricane warning systems that can greatly reduce the consequences of natural disasters, including training for scientists, risk assessment and such things as satellite weather reports to help them track storms that may be headed their way.

Scientists and engineers around the world have made great advances in earthquake engineering. It is, of course, unfeasible physically to move cities such as Tokyo and San Francisco that have been built in earthquake zones, but most often it is not the earthquake that kills people, it is the collapsing buildings, bridges and other structures that cause deaths, and the likelihood of that happening can be greatly reduced by better building programmes.

Finally, perhaps we need to consider the natural disaster that we are causing ourselves. Through our mismanagement of the planet's resources we have catapulted hundreds of species of plants and animals into extinction, at the same time possibly wrecking our own long-term prospects for survival. Maybe this is one disaster that could be averted if we are willing to act with a sense of responsibility.

THE MOVING EARTH

The Earth's outer crust is not a solid sheet but is made up of between 12 and 15 separate pieces called tectonic plates. These plates are constantly moving. Some are colliding, some are moving apart and some slide alongside one another. These plates are moving very slowly but over time great stresses build up in the rocks along the edges of the plates. Eventually the rocks cannot be stretched or folded any more and they snap and shift, sending out shock waves as they do so. This sudden shifting of rocks in the crust is what we call an earthquake.

Enormous energy is released from the focus of the earthquake, the place where the greatest movement occurs, which can be deep beneath the Earth. The shock waves spread out from it like ripples in a pond. The point on the surface closest to the focus is called the epicentre and it is here that the most damage will be done.

Faults in the Earth's crust are caused by the movements of the tectonic plates.

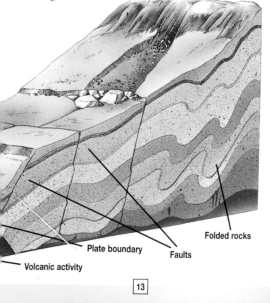

Folded rocks

Plate boundary

Faults

Volcanic activity

EARTHQUAKE ZONES

Over one million earthquakes occur every year but most of these are too small to notice. Most of them happen along fairly well defined earthquake belts, which follow the edges of the plates. Over half of the world's worst earthquakes happen around the Pacific Rim in belts that stretch from Japan, down to the South Pacific, and along the

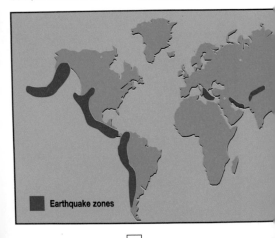

■ Earthquake zones

coast of California and into South America. An earthquake can happen on land or under water.

A major quake may last for only a minute but in that time it can kill thousands of people and destroy complete towns and villages. After the main shock there can be further smaller waves called aftershocks. When shock waves move through solid rock they come to a stop once the rocks stop moving. However, when they move through sand and sediment they break up the material, which moves like a liquid. This causes an enormous amount of damage.

Mapping the world's earthquake zones also shows where the boundaries between the tectonic plates lie. For instance, the earthquake zone that stretches along the length of the Americas marks where the Pacific plate collides with the North and South American plates.

MEASURING EARTHQUAKES

In 1935 Charles Richter
devised a scale that
measured the magnitude
or size of an earthquake.
The Richter scale is a
logarithmic scale, which
means that an increase of
1 on the scale corresponds
to a tenfold increase in
magnitude, so that an
earthquake registering 5
will be a hundred times
more powerful than one
measuring 3. It is possible
for a very small tremor to
register less than zero on
the scale and be given a
minus number. Magnitude
7 has the equivalent
power of 1 million tons of
TNT.

Earthquakes are also
measured using the
Mercalli scale. In 1902
Guiseppe Mercalli worked
out a scale of damage
from Degree I, which is

hardly felt at all, to Degree XII, which can cause total destruction. The Mercalli scale measures an earthquake's strength in terms of its effects rather than its magnitude.

The Chinese were the first to invent a device for detecting earthquakes. When it was shaken by vibrations from a distant quake a ball fell from one of the dragon's mouths into a frog's mouth.

In the early hours of the morning of 18 April 1906 people in San Francisco were suddenly thrown to the ground as one of history's most famous natural disasters struck and the buildings around them collapsed. The streets were described as moving like 'waves of water'. Building after building was levelled, church spires buckled and fell and one hotel simply folded up, crushing to death all 80 people inside it. Over 450 people died in all. The worst damage to property in the city occurred in the downtown area. The whole of Chinatown was destroyed and only one building was left standing on the top of Nob Hill. A number of fires broke out, fed by escapes from ruptured gas pipes, and by noon on the first day they were raging out of control. At the time damage caused by the earthquake was estimated at around £7 million with fire damage at £140 million. The quake measured 7.8 on the Richter scale and happened when the San Andreas fault, which runs from Mexico to northern California, suddenly jumped 4.5 to 6 metres (15-20 feet), releasing huge amounts of stored energy.

TOKYO, 1923

On 1 September 1923 three massive 8.3 magnitude shocks, the most powerful earthquake to strike the area for 70 years, hit the cities of Tokyo and Yokohama. Huge waves swamped the bay area of Tokyo and oil tanks exploded. Only about 1 per cent of Tokyo's buildings were severely damaged by the quake but massive fires broke out and swept across the wood and paper houses in the city. Of the

140,000 people who died in the disaster the vast majority were victims of the fire. Over 200,000 buildings burned down, leaving more than half a million people homeless. Many people tried to escape the flames by running into the grounds around the Imperial Palace or jumping into canals. September 1st is now designated as Disaster Prevention Day in Japan and earthquake drills are held in preparation for the inevitable next big quake during which volunteers are shown how to put out fires and use emergency equipment.

AGADIR, 1960

On the evening of 29 February 1960 a massive earthquake hit the city of Agadir in Morocco. A minor tremor had hit the city earlier that week giving some warning of the disaster to come but little could be done to prepare for the devastating shock that struck, leaving the city in ruins. A giant wave rushed 300 metres inshore from the buckling floor of the Mediterranean causing huge damage. Hotels built for tourists buckled and fell like houses of cards. Lines of communication

were cut and the city was plunged into darkness. Water mains burst in great fountains, every fire station was destroyed and there was no one to fight the hundreds of fires that ignited. Miraculously, the city airport was undamaged by the earthquake and a fleet of 75 aircraft shuttled the wounded to safety. Several warships from a number of countries, including Britain and France, also helped. Around 12,000 people were declared dead with many more missing. The damage was so extensive that the area was simply bulldozed and abandoned.

GUATEMALA, 1976

On 4 February 1976 the Central American country of Guatemala was struck by a massive earthquake that shuddered along the Carribean and North American plate boundary. Striking at 3 a.m., the quake caught people asleep in bed who, with no warning, were unable to escape from their homes and were buried beneath the rubble as buildings collapsed around them.

Landslides triggered by the earthquake caused further damage, shattering bridges, sweeping away livestock and people and burying whole villages beneath a wave of rubble. Rivers were dammed by avalanches and spilled over their banks, flooding the surrounding countryside.

In Guatemala City huge fissures opened up in the streets and many buildings were demolished,

including hospitals and almost a third of the homes in the city. In all 22,000 people died and over a million survivors, around one in five of the population, were made homeless.

VOLCANOES

Deep beneath the Earth's crust there are pockets of partially liquid rock called magma that is under enormous pressure and temperature. Magma may rise up through the rocks of the crust. Often it solidifies before it reaches the surface, however, if the magma does break through to the surface, the result is a volcano. Magma that reaches the surface is called lava

Volcanoes most often occur at plate boundaries. If two plates separate the crust is weakened and the magma can escape more easily. Also, if two plates collide one may be forced beneath the other where it melts and a massive eruption occurs as the melted material explodes out. Volcanoes can form beneath the ocean as well as on land.

A volcano's cone is built up from ash and lava that

accumulates over the years. The shape the volcano takes depends on how fast the lava flows from it. As the fast moving lava flows down the slopes it cools and hardens. Most lavas cool to form a rock called basalt.

A volcano is like a channel leading to a reservoir of molten rock deep beneath the surface.

ERUPTIONS

Not all volcanic eruptions are violent. Some volcanoes produce flood lavas, which slowly flow out in huge quantities to cover large areas of land. Almost all of Iceland is made up of flood lava. Hawaiian eruptions, such as those typical of the islands, are similar although the lava may be faster flowing and there may be gas explosions. The simplest form of explosive eruption is

Strombolian. Volcanic bombs (lumps of lava) and gas can be thrown in to the air in a series of mild explosions that may come every few seconds. Vulcanian volcanoes occur where a plug of exposed lava soldifies and blocks the volcano's vent. Eventually the pressure of the gases and molten rock building up behind the plug overwhelms it and there is an explosion of rock vapour and ash as the plug is blown apart.

Mount Pinatubo in the Philippines erupted in a massive explosion in 1991.

In the afternoon of August 24 AD 79 Mount Vesuvius on the island of Sicily erupted sending out a huge cloud of glowing ash and barraging the surrounding country with showers of rock. For 28 hours the volcano continued to pour out rock and ash until the city of Pompeii and its unfortunate inhabitants was buried under 7 metres

(23 feet) of rock and ash. Two thousand people died in the catastrophe.

The town of Pompeii lay hidden and forgotten until 1631 when Vesuvius erupted again and workers discovered some Roman coins. Over the course of the next 200 years or so various artefacts were dug up and looted. The site was cleared and slowly more and more was uncovered. Eventually the importance of the discoveries was realized and efforts were made to preserve the site. Today it is possible to visit Pompeii and walk down the streets and still see the figures in the same positions as they were when the ash enveloped them over 1900 years ago.

Situated on the eastern side of Sicily, Mount Etna is the highest active volcano in Europe and has erupted as recently as 1979 and 1983. The volcano is thought to have been active for over two million years. When Etna erupts red hot lava pours down the side of the mountain destroying everything in its path. Because a number of people live close to the volcano they have developed ways of diverting the lava flow. This has included building walls that stopped some of the damage caused by the molten rock. The first attempt to do this was in 1669 when, after three days of earth-quakes, Mount Etna began the most violent eruption in its recorded history. A huge lava flow began moving towards the town of Catania. For three days an 18-metre (60-foot) high stone wall held back the flow until it finally gave way and tons of lava flowed through the gap, devastating the town.

Mount Etna has been active throughout its two-million-year existence.

KRAKATOA, 1883

On August 27 1883 the volcanic island of Krakatoa, which lay between the islands of Java and Sumatra, erupted with what may be the loudest explosion ever heard in recorded history. It was heard nearly 4800 kilometres (3000 miles) away. Six cubic kilometres of dust and ash shot 80 kilometres (50 miles) into the atmosphere. This immense cloud circled much of the Earth, blocking the sun and causing a worldwide temperature drop. A 37-metre (120-foot) high tsunami spread out from the eruption, sinking a number of ships and drowning 36,000 people. On Batavia, about 160 kilometres (100 miles) away, it rained thick black mud and elsewhere ash covered the ground at over a metre an hour. Three-quarters of the island were blasted away in the explosion. Today a new volcano, Anak Krakatoa, the child of Krakatoa, has grown up on the site.

MOUNT ST HELENS, 1980

Just after 8.30 on the
morning of 18 May 1980
Mount St Helens in the
western state of
Washington, USA,
erupted. The explosion
was so loud that it could
be heard over 300
kilometres (190 miles)
away. Towns 160
kilometres (100 miles)
from the eruption were
covered in choking ash
that turned day into night
and created some of the
most spectacular sunsets
seen in recent years.
People as far away as 16
kilometres (10 miles) were
thrown out of bed and
police closed all roads up
to 80 kilometres (50 miles)
from the mountain. The
explosion caused a huge
black cloud of dust and
ash and a layer up to 10
centimetres (4 inches)
deep fell on towns in

Oregon and Washington State. This massive cloud moved round the world in just 17 days and there were fears that average global temperatures might drop by one degree. The amount of damage caused has been estimated at over £1 billion.

TSUNAMIS

These giant waves, sometimes called seismic waves, most commonly start when the shock waves from an earthquake leave the sea bed and come to the surface. Tsunamis can also be generated by massive landslides or volcanic eruptions. Vibrations travel out from the epicentre of the quake at over 750 km/h (470 mph) for thousands of kilometres. They can go unnoticed in open water but as they approach shallow water they slow down and increase in height, producing vast waves as much as 76 metres (250 feet) high. These can produce devastating results on low lying areas. Areas at risk include many of the coral islands in the Pacific and the heavily populated coastline of Japan. In 1964 waves from an Alaskan earthquake travelled as far as California and Japan. Special centres send out messages to warn high risk areas of possible tsunamis after an earthquake. Sometimes mistakenly called tidal waves, tsunamis have nothing to do with tides.

A small ship caught at sea by a tsunami will have little chance of survival.

FLOODS

When it rains, the water may soak into the ground, fall into rivers and streams or simply evaporate. One of the quickest ways for water to get into rivers is by surface run off. This happens when water falls on hard rock that is unable to soak it up. The water runs off the rock to produce streams which then become rivers. If there is a large run off the rivers may be unable to cope with the added amount of water and overflow their banks causing floods. An increase in surface run off can be caused by heavy falls of snow on high ground or long periods of rain. In dry weather there can be flash floods. These are caused by a sudden heavy rainfall on to a hard surface. In 1993 over 20 people died in a flash flood in Ohio, USA.

Flooding can also be caused by high seas and strong winds. Often coastal defences cannot cope with extreme conditions and sea water floods the land.

Unusually heavy rainfall can cause river to over-flow their banks, flooding the country around.

HOLLAND, 1953

The Dutch are experts at reclaiming land from the sea and keeping out floodwater and over the years they have built a number of defences against flooding. In February 1953 their skills were put to the test when fifty of Holland's sea dykes were breached in a single night and the sea poured through. Hurricane winds of over 160 km/h (100 mph) pushed water from the Atlantic into the North Sea sending abnormally high tides and waves against the dykes. More than a hundred towns vanished under water. Around 1800 people were drowned and there was considerable damage to property. Seventy-two thousand people had to be evacuated from their homes. Three thousand houses were totally destroyed. Hundreds of square kilometres of agricultural land were ruined by salt water. After the floodwaters had gone down a massive clear-up operation was begun. People from 25 countries helped fly in food and medical supplies to the stricken Dutch.

FLORENCE UNDER FLOOD, 1966

In 1966, Europe suffered extremely bad weather when gales and storms lashed France, Switzerland, Germany and Italy. Strong winds brought enormous amounts of rain along the whole length of Italy and in Florence, on 3rd and

4th November, they had more than a third of their average annual rainfall in just two days. The River Arno burst its banks, rising over 5 metres (16 feet) in the city. Water began cascading through the city making 5000 families homeless and swamping many of the famous buildings.

Six hundred paintings were under water for hours at the Uffizi Gallery and over six million books were damaged or destroyed. Thousands of priceless art treasures were lost or irreparably damaged as hundreds of thousands of tons of mud were deposited within the city.

Thirty-five people drowned in the city and over a hundred more in the surrounding country-side. After the floods receded volunteers from all over the world came to help with the rescue operations and to try to restore the damaged works of art.

VAIONT DAM, 1963

This disaster would fit into several categories – earthquake, avalanche and flood. The Vaiont Dam is in the north-eastern part of Italy, high up in the mountains. On 9 October 1963 an earthquake sent massive landslides tumbling down the sides of the mountains on either side of the dam. Rocks poured into the lake and within minutes the displaced water was cascading over the top forming a waterfall 460 metres (1500 feet) high. People who survived the disaster say they heard a sound like thunder, as the water poured out. At first it was thought that the dam had burst, but it was not until the next morning that it was possible to see what had really happened. When the dam was examined the only damaged section was found to be along the top of the wall. Many of the villages below the dam were destroyed and over 4000 people died, their bodies carried up to 60 kilometres (40 miles) downstream by the force of the torrent.

During the three months of August, September and October 1988 severe monsoon rains swept across India and Southeast Asia. Destruction of the forests in the Himalayas had removed one of the natural defences against flooding and the waters swept unimpeded down the mountains. The Ganges, which flows across the plains of Bangladesh, frequently floods but this year the damage was colossal. Defences that had been built to hold back the water were overwhelmed as three-quarters of the country disappeared under water.

UN officials described it as one of the 'worst natural disasters of the century' as an estimated 5000 people drowned and more than half the population were left homeless. Disease compounded the misery as three million people fell ill from diarrhoea and dysentery. The economy of Bangladesh practically came to a standstill as factories and equipment were destroyed and 85 per cent of the population became unemployed. Even months later villages were still cut off by the flood waters.

In the 1990s a Flood Action Plan was started with the aim of controlling river flooding. Experts from around the world are lending their help. However, given the scale of the problem, it is unlikely that a solution will soon be found.

TORNADOES

Tornadoes are very powerful whirlwinds that move in an irregular pattern, making them hard to track. They are similar to hurricanes in that they form when a funnel of warm air is sucked up from the ground towards cold air, perhaps in a thundercloud. They can, however, be far more dangerous than a hurricane: the highest windspeeds ever measured, 500 km/h (310mph), have been recorded in a tornado.

Tornadoes are most common in the USA where they are known as twisters; over 500 may appear during spring and early summer. Nothing is safe in the path of a tornado, which might travel 200 kilometres (125 miles) before running out of energy. Tornadoes are short-lived, lasting for no more than two hours and perhaps as little as 10 minutes, but in that time they can cause chaos. Cars, trees and animals can be sucked into the air and buildings may explode outwards as the air pressure outside drops alarmingly as a tornado rips its way across the countryside devastating everything in its path.

THE GREAT TORNADOES OF '74

On 3rd and 4th April 1974 148 tornadoes swept across 13 states and 4200 km (2600 miles) of the USA all the way from Alabama to the Canadian border in a 24-hour period that brought widespread destruction but relatively little loss of life.

Six of the tornadoes were among the largest ever recorded. Ten thousand homes were destroyed by winds that ripped through them at up to 400 km/h (250 mph). In Louisville, Kentucky, 900 homes were torn apart in just 20 minutes. Xenia, in Ohio, was practically obliterated with 3000 homes being damaged or destroyed in a town of just 27,000 inhabitants. The bill for damages from the tornadoes came to around $500 million. That the death toll was kept down to 315 was almost entirely thanks to the efficiency of the tornado warning services who made sure that people had as much time as possible to prepare before the winds struck.

Waterspouts can form in a variety of conditions – summer or winter, night or day, on cold days or on hot. From a cloudy sky a funnel-shaped mass of air descends towards the water surface. Beneath it the water begins to foam and spray rises to meet the funnel. Eventually, the rising water and descending air meet and the waterspout is formed.

Water spouts can reach an extraordinary height. The highest spout ever recorded, formed off New South Wales in 1898, was reliably measured at 1542 metres (5014 feet) high.

The spout may move slowly across the water surface or it may travel at speeds of 80km/h (50 mph). Within the spout the wind may whirl at up to 320 km/h (200 mph).

A tornado passing over water can turn into a waterspout, during which time it can wreck small boats, before becoming a tornado again when it returns to dry land.

Sailing ships are particularly vulnerable to waterspouts – a small ship can be capsized or wrecked by the whirling winds and sudden deluge of water ripping off masts and sails. In 1969 people in Boca Grande Key, Florida, watched helplessly as a waterspout approached and uprooted the concrete shelter that they had taken refuge in, lifting them and the shelter a metre off the ground.

HURRICANES

Hurricanes form when the temperature exceeds 27°C (80°F) over the ocean. As large amounts of water evaporate, the vapour rises up forming a spiral shape. More air is sucked in to join the base of the hurricane. This build up increases the amount of water in the clouds above. At the centre, or eye, of the hurricane the air is calm but the winds spiralling around the outside can exceed 300

The eye

km/h (185 mph). The hurricane season in the northern hemisphere is from August until October whilst in the south, where they are called typhoons, it runs from December to May. Giving names to individual hurricanes is an idea that was introduced by an Australian called Clement Wragge. It is said that he gave them the names of women he didn't like! Nowadays a list of alternating male and female names is drawn up every year and each hurricane is allocated a name as it is detected.

Anatomy of a hurricane. Air is sucked up from the ocean and spirals towards the eye of the hurricane

Torrential rain

HURRICANE GILBERT, 1988

In 1988, the worst hurricane ever recorded swept across the Caribbean with wind speeds of up to 320 km/h (200 mph). Hurricane Gilbert began its life off the coast of Africa and travelled across the Atlantic gathering strength as it did so. On 11September it reached the southern tip of Haiti. Ten people were drowned and the entire banana crop was destroyed. The next morning Gilbert blasted into Jamaica. Half a millon people were left homeless as storm damage made four out of five homes uninhabitable.

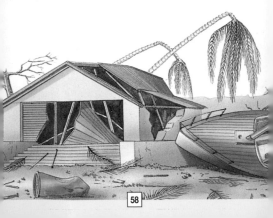

The hurricane swept on, its strength unabated. Mexico, Nicaragua, Honduras and Guatemala reported deaths and destruction of crops and property. Winds gusting at 350 km/h (218 mph) sent huge waves crashing over the shore of the Yucatan Peninsula of Mexico. Dozens of tornadoes produced by Gilbert spread through Texas, ripping off roofs and over-turning vehicles. In all, some $10 billion worth of damage was credited to Hurricane Gilbert. Almost three-quarters of a million people were made homeless and 350 lost their lives.

WINTER STORM, 1993

In March 1993 the east coast of the United States was enveloped in a ferocious snowstorm. The origins of the storm were in the Gulf of Mexico on 12 March when temperatures dropped below freezing, tides rose to 6 metres (20 feet) above their normal levels and hurricane winds began to blow.

Gaining in strength, the storm headed north across Florida wiping out acres of citrus crops as it passed over the Sunshine State. Thirty centimetres (12 inches) of snow fell on northern Georgia, 38 centimetres (15 inches) on Alabama and 53 centimetres (21 inches) in Tennessee. As the storm continued on its track airports were closed and travellers stranded as roads were blocked by huge snowdrifts. Towns along the northeast coast were evacuated and power lines were downed by the hurricane winds. Over a billion dollars of damage was caused and 500 people died as a result of a storm that one weather forecaster described as a 'snowacane'.

The East Coast cities of America were brought to a standstill by heavy snowfalls.

DROUGHT

Drought occurs when moisture disappears through evaporation faster than it is replaced by rain. A drought may happen in any climate zone, from tropical to tundra. Permanent drought is a feature in parts of Australia, Africa, Central and South America and Asia where the climate is continually dry and there is little irrigation. Parts of the Atacama Desert in Chile have recorded no rain at all for over 400 years! Unpredictable droughts occur when expected rainfall fails to materialise, resulting in poor plant growth, increased erosion and famine. Some of the worst droughts of this century occurred in the mid 1980s in the Sahel region of West Africa when the summer rains failed.

Water shortages can also affect the countries of Europe and North America as, happened in 1976 when Britain faced the worst recorded drought in its history, coupled with temperatures rising up past 30°C, and tankers had to be employed to carry water to some towns.

THE GREAT DUST BOWL

One of the greatest droughts of modern times occurred in the mid-western United States between 1934 and 1941. The causes of the disaster were not entirely natural as unwise farming practices also played a part. During the First World War farmers expanded their fields to take advantage of soaring wheat prices. After the war, prices fell again, how-ever, and large numbers of cattle were turned into the ploughed fields. Millions of hooves crumbled the soil and the winter winds blew it away. From 1934 drought conditions made matters worse. Dust lifted up from the land in 300-metre (1000-foot) high clouds that swept over farms and suffocated animals in storms that lasted for days. In the summer, desert heat baked the land in conditions that were too much even for rattlesnakes to survive. Nineteen states felt the effects of the drought.

The rains finally returned in 1940 but not before people in their thousands had left their homes in a hopeless search for work.

FAMINE

A disaster that is often linked with drought is the problem of famine. Between 1984 and 1985 ten million people in Africa were forced to abandon their land because of drought and in 1992 over 50 per cent of the crops failed in eight of the countries in the Horn of Africa. Floods, of course, can also bring famine if farming land is inundated and crops washed away.

One country that has suffered a great deal from famine is Ethiopia. The loss of good soil due to overfarming has resulted in the over-use of the little land that remains. This, combined with long periods of drought, has brought the country to crisis point.

Famine also occurs when food plants are attacked by pests and disease. In the 1840s Ireland was struck three times by a fungal blight that destroyed most of the potato crop. As potatoes provided over 80 per cent of the calories needed by the poor, the effect was dramatic. It is estimated that over a million people died and the same number emigrated, reducing the population in Ireland by 25 per cent.

It perhaps ought to be pointed out that very often human causes of famine can sometimes far outweigh natural causes. In Cambodia in the 1970s the policies of the Khmer Rouge regime led to the deaths by starvation of a million or more people.

A PLAGUE OF LOCUSTS

Locusts are large forms of grasshopper that are found all over Africa and the Middle East. The best known varieties are the desert locust, which is found from North Africa to India, and the migratory locust, found in grasslands in Africa, Eurasia, Australia and New Zealand. Plagues of migrating locusts can cause devastation,

destroying crops and plants over a wide area. A swarm can sometimes travel a distance of over 3000 kilometres (1875 miles). A single swarm can cover an area of 5000 sq km (3125 sq miles). Because they are so wide-ranging and move in such huge numbers locusts are nearly impossible to control. Some methods that have been tried include destroying the eggs, spraying swarms with insecticides and digging trenches to trap the young locusts before they can fly.

LANDSLIDES AND AVALANCHES

Landslides and avalanches happen when large amounts of rock, mud and other loose materials are suddenly uprooted and sent sliding down a slope. This might be caused by an earthquake or it might happen after heavy rain or when soil becomes water-logged after a fall of snow.

As the material loses its grip and begins to move down the slope it gathers speed and sweeps up more material with devastating results. Nepal suffers from frequent landslides because the hillsides have been stripped of trees. When it rains the water soaks into the soil and this slides down the mountain-side. Much of the damage after the explosion on Mount St Helens in the USA was caused by falling

rock mixed with ice and snow, which thundered down the side of the mountain in the biggest avalanche ever recorded. The debris travelled at 400 km/h (250 mph)!

In 1955 the town of Nicolet in Canada was badly damaged when a large section of the terrace the town stands on slid into the Nicolet River leaving a crater 185 metres (600 feet) across.

ABERFAN, 1966

The worst landslide in Wales' history came about with the collapse of an artificial mountain on 21 October 1966.

A 250-metre (800-foot) high mountain of waste material from the local coalmine had been piled up outside the village of Aberfan. Without warning, two million tonnes of rock, coal and mud began to move with a thunderous roar towards the local school, uprooting trees and crushing houses. The huge mass of material struck the school with terrible force. It was the start of the school day and almost every child in the village was there. The building was knocked from its foundations, collapsing under the weight of the avalanche, which crushed children and their teachers beneath it.

One hundred and forty-five people, among them 116 children, lost their lives. According to a geologist the cause of the disaster was an underground spring that formed beneath the slag heap and destabilized it.

SNOW DANGER

Snow avalanches may be started by the slightest movement, perhaps of small amounts of snow dislodged by the weight of skiers, by animals, a passing jet or even by thunder. They can also be caused by new snow falling on old, weakening the older snow below.

The avalanche collects more and more snow as it moves down the mountainside, an estimate of 2.5 million tons has been made for one in the Italian Alps. This huge weight of snow can be travelling at great speed across a front 1.5 km (1 mile) wide. Avalanches in the Alps have been timed at 480km/h (300 mph). The wind ahead of the avalanche front can travel even faster. Trees and buildings can be blown aside by 120 metres (400 feet) per second blasts. It is possible for an avalanche to be travelling so fast that it can roar down one side of a valley and up the other.

During the First World War it is thought that between 40,000 and 80,000 people lost their lives in avalanches triggered in the Tyrolean Alps by the sound of gunfire, more than were directly killed by all the bullets and shells fired in this part of Europe.

Avalanche control programmes using, for example, controlled explosions to remove the snow in small chunks, are used to lessen the risks of avalanche in many places.

SUBSIDENCE

Ground subsidence, the collapse of the earth's surface, can take place for a number of reasons. A very small area may suddenly collapse, or a whole city – Venice is a good example – may slowly sink. The rate at which Venice is sinking has been increasing in recent years. This has probably been the result of an increasing amount of water being pumped from the wells that supply the city. The reduction in water pressure beneath the surface brought about greater subsidence as the ground sank. The pumping has now been halted but Venice continues to sink, albeit more slowly. Earthquakes may also be a cause of subsidence – the 1964 Alaskan earthquake caused widespread movements along Alaska's south shore.

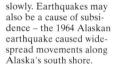

Subsidence also arises when limestone and other soluble rocks are gradually dissolved deep underground, resulting in the collapse of the surface above. This type of subsidence is a problem particularly in the southeastern United States where there are extensive limestone deposits.

Human activities, for example mining, can cause subsidence. In Cheshire, salt mining brought about frequent collapses of the buildings above the mines. However, the inhabitants, recognizing the risks, built timber houses that could be jacked back up again.

A shower of large hailstones, perhaps as heavy as half a kilogram (1 lb) apiece, can do substantial damage. They are formed in the coldest regions of thunderclouds where water droplets freeze. The icy droplets sink through the cloud, collecting more droplets and growing in size. Powerful air currents in the cloud send the growing hailstones back up again and more coatings of ice are added. In a particularly strong updraught very large stones, bigger than cricket balls, may form.

Hail can be a severe hazard for pilots. A light aircraft flying through a thunderstorm can be wrecked by hail and larger craft can have their windshields smashed by rock hard lumps of ice travelling at almost 300 km/h (190 mph).

Crops and livestock can be devastated by hail – in July 1978 more than 200 sheep were killed in Montana, USA, by hailstones the size of baseballs In 1928, in Romania, six children died when they were caught in a storm of hail as large as hen's eggs.

METEORITES

Meteoroids are the debris left over from the formation of the planets and from comets in the Solar System. It has been estimated that over 100,000 million meteoroids strike the Earth's atmosphere every day. Usually these are very tiny and burn up before they get anywhere

near the ground, leaving the characteristic bright trail called a shooting star.

On rare occasions the Earth is struck by a large meteorite. In Arizona there is a crater over one kilometre (0.6 miles) wide that was made by a meteorite weighing around 70,000 tons about 25,000 years ago. In 1908 a fragment of a comet landed in the Tunguska forest in central Siberia producing an explosion that could be heard over 500 kilometres (310 miles) away.

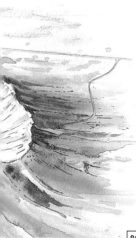

Scientists believe that a huge meteorite over 20 kilometres (12.5 miles) wide hit the Earth 65 million years ago, resulting in a dust cloud that covered the planet. Without sunlight or warmth plants died followed by the animals who had nothing to eat. This, some say, is how dinosaurs disappeared from the Earth.

It can only be a matter of time before another big meteorite strikes the Earth. Keep watching the sky!

THE BLACK DEATH

The Black Death first appeared in Europe on the island of Sicily in 1347 and soon spread to most of the continent. In a short time, swellings appeared on the victim's neck and under the armpits and dark patches covered the body, hence the name the Black Death. The unfortunate person was usually dead within three days. Some people wore charms to protect themselves.

Others beat themselves and asked for forgiveness, thinking the plague to be a punishment from God. Many left the towns and went into the countryside hoping to escape infection. By the end of 1348 a third of the population of Europe were dead. Blood-sucking fleas living on black rats were the carriers of the plague, a fact that was unknown to the people of the time. The rats travelled in the holds of ships, bringing the fleas with them. The fleas bit humans who then fell ill. The Black Death lasted for several hundred years, disappearing for a while and then resurfacing. In 1665 in London over 68,000 people died. The end of the Black Death in Britain came in 1666 when a number of factors, including the Great Fire of London and improved standards of hygiene stopped its spread.

EPIDEMICS

Diseases may not be the most spectacular of the natural disasters that can afflict mankind but in terms of the numbers of people affected they can be among the most devastating. Following the enormous loss of life that had been inflicted during the First World War the great flu epidemic that swept across the Earth in 1918-19 brought a further wave of misery to an already shaken world.

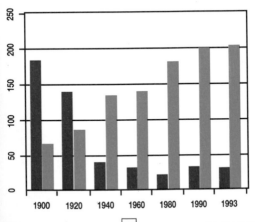

More than 22 million people died in the 16 months the epidemic lasted, more than in the whole of the First World War, with victims all over the world. No one has been able to establish where the epidemic originated. Some say Chinese labourers brought it to Europe, others that it started in Spain (the disease was sometimes known as Spanish Influenza), others blamed Russian soldiers from Vladivostok.

Wherever it arose the arrival of the epidemic in the USA has been pinpointed. A sailor arriving back from Europe on a troop transport brought the infection to Boston on 28 August 1918. Within four months 15,000 people were dead in Massachusetts. In all, over half a million died in the United States. Some experts believe that the next major epidemic is already overdue.

Opposite is a graph that shows how the number of deaths per 100,000 members of the population owing to influenza (shown in red) has fallen dramatically in the United States this century. Also shown on the graph is the rising number of deaths caused by cancer in America (in green). Unlike the vaccinations available for influenza protection no truly effective treatment for cancer has yet been found.

Another fear that many doctors and scientists have is that there may be a reappearance of illnesses such as tuberculosis that for many years were thought to have been eliminated, as new drug resistant strains appear.

THE HUMAN RACE?

The final choice of disaster may, at first sight, seem an odd one. Yet the human race is undeniably a natural phenomenon and for the hundreds of species that have become extinct through exploitatfon and the destruction of their habitats humans have definitely been a disaster. Almost certainly no earthquake or volcano ever wiped out an entire

species. More than half of the world's tropical rain-forests have already been destroyed and in just a few decades they, and the countless known and unknown species they contain, may be gone forever. The hole in the ozone layer, the green-house effect and acid rain are all caused by things we do, and the consequences of our actions are felt all over the world. Perhaps we should think seriously about the way we are treating the world before we discover that we are the biggest disaster of all.

GLOSSARY

aftershock: Minor shock following an earthquake as rocks readjust.

avalanche: Rapid movement of snow and ice down mountain slopes, sometimes taking a great deal of rock with it.

crust: Outer layer of the Earth, between 6 and 60 km (4 to 40 miles) thick.

deforestation: Total felling and clearing of a forest by human activity.

desert: Area where rainfall is scant or absent altogether and does not exceed water lost by evaporation.

desertification: Extending of deserts into areas where they did not previously exist, often as a result of over-grazing and the clearance of scrub land, leaving the land vulnerable to erosion.

drought: Lengthy period during which little or no precipitation occurs.

earthquake: Movement in the Earth's crust causing rocks to buckle and fracture. Most earthquake activity occurs along the boundaries of tectonic plates. The centre of an earthquake is called its focus.

epicentre: Point on the Earth's surface directly above an earthquake focus.

fault: Fracture in the Earth's crust along which rocks have moved. Movement during an earthquake may range from a few centimetres to several metres.

flash-flood: Rapid rise of the water level in a river due to heavy rain or the collapse of an obstruction such as a dam. Flash-floods can be of great power and may cause much damage.

hail: Particles of ice that fall from thunderclouds. Rising currents of air keep the hailstones up while they add extra layers of ice until they are large enough to fall through the cloud.

hurricane: Tropical cyclone with wind speeds in excess of 120 km/h (75mph) accompanied by torrential rain and lightning in the North Atlantic, Caribbean Sea and Gulf of Mexico. A hurricane system can vary between 100 to 1600 km(62.5 to 1000 miles) across . Tropical cyclones in the Pacific area are known as typhoons.

landslide: Sudden movement downslope of a body of rock or earth. This may come about as a result of heavy rain, or through an earthquake, or by human interference.

lava: Molten material that flows from an erupting volcano on to the surface of the Earth where it cools and solidifies.

magma: Molten rock existing at depths greater than 16 kilometres (10 miles) below the Earth's surface. Magma that reaches the surface through volcanoes or fissures in the ground is called lava.

Mercalli scale: Scale for measuring the intensity of an earthquake in terms of visible damage and devastation. Earthquakes labelled I–VI are minor, VI–VIII are damaging, VIII–X are destructive and X–XII are major. For example, VI is 'Felt by all, many frightened and run indoors. Some heavy furniture moved…' and XI has 'Few if any structures remain standing. Bridges destroyed… '

plate tectonics: The outer 100 km (62.5 miles) or so of the Earth is split into a series of moving plates. Where the plates join there are earthquakes and volcanic activity. Where an oceanic plate collides with another oceanic plate an arc of volcanic islands is formed as the crust is pushed upwards.

Richter scale: Scale devised by the American C.F. Richter in 1935 to measure the magnitude of an earthquake. It is more precise than the Mercalli scale because it depends on instrumental measures using a seis-mometer. No earthquake measuring more than 8.9 has ever been recorded.

Sahel: Zone of semi-desert along the southern fringe of the Sahara where droughts occur frequently, causing regular crop failures and famine.

tornado: Rapidly spinning column of air with violent winds in excess of 300 km/h (190 mph) accompanied by violent downdraughts. Tornadoes are common in the midwest of the USA where they cause extensive damage.

tsunami: A large sea wave generated by an earthquake or a violent volcanic eruption at or below sea level. Tsunamis can cross the ocean at between 600 and 900 km/h (375 and 560 mph) and reach heights in excess of 15m (50ft) on entering shallow coastal water.

volcano: Opening in the Earth's crust connected by a channel to a magma chamber from which lava, gases and fragments of rock and ash are ejected.

waterspout: Oceanic equivalent of a tornado, but not of the same intensity or duration. Water is sucked up from the surface by the powerful updraughts and this may be released as an immense deluge if the waterspout crosses the shore.